HERBY ALICE COUNTS DOWN TO YESTERDAY

A one-act comedy by
Nicole B. Adkins

www.youthplays.com
info@youthplays.com
424-703-5315

COPYRIGHT RULES TO REMEMBER

CAST OF CHARACTERS

This play can be performed with as few as 10 actors (3 females, 3 males, 4 either), or there can be as many students and aliens as the producing company wishes.

The lines that belong to Aliens 1 and 2 could be distributed between a larger cast of Aliens.

All adult roles may be performed by youth.

STUDENTS:

ROSE PLUM, girl.

HERBY ALICE, boy.

CLARISSA, girl.

STUDENT 1, gender flexible.*

STUDENT 2, gender flexible.*

COOL STUDENT, boy.

DORKY STUDENT, boy.*

CAMERA GUY, gender flexible.

ADULTS & ALIENS:

MRS. PRATTLE, female teacher.

DR. FARAWAY, gender flexible, principal/gym coach.

DR. TOMORROW, gender flexible, mad scientist.*

ALIEN 1, gender flexible.*

ALIEN 2, gender flexible.*

*Possible Doublings:

STUDENT 1/ALIEN 1
STUDENT 2/ALIEN 2
DORKY STUDENT/DR. TOMORROW

PRODUCTION NOTES

There should be no blackouts between scenes. Scene headings are only provided for the purpose of making larger beats clear. Action should flow smoothly and continually, building throughout the play all the way from "ten" to launch.

The spacecraft revealed at the end, as well as the pieces of it we see beforehand, can be as suggested or literal as the producing company wishes. Use your imagination—have fun with this!

SCENE 1

(DR. FARAWAY, School Principal and Gym Coach, enters decidedly. He steps into the empty frame of a full-length mirror. He addresses the audience.)

DR. FARAWAY: We are what we are, and we say what we say, speeding faster than light into yester-today...

(Dr. Faraway exits, as HERBY ALICE, a student and rocket scientist, enters. Herby wears a necktie as usual. He is completely focused on fixing a component of a high-tech contraption he is building. He stands in the mirror frame. CLARISSA, lead student reporter, enters. She is brushing her perfect hair and powdering her perfect nose. She is followed by two more students: CAMERA GUY, and media hopeful, ROSE PLUM. Rose takes notes.)

CLARISSA: *(To Rose:)* How do I look?

ROSE: Um...I would bet the thermal properties of your blazer are exceptionally beneficial in algid weather.

CLARISSA: *(Sighs:)* You *are* a fixer-upper, aren't you?

ROSE: I meant —

(Clarissa takes the microphone from Rose.)

CLARISSA: Rose, if it is really your plan to permanently join the ranks of our elite on-camera team, you are going to have to work on your delivery. Remember what happened the *first time*. Observe the following. Take notes. *(To Camera Guy:)* Let's roll!

(Clarissa stands next to Herby. Camera Guy trains his Camera on them.)

Good morning, studs and 'ents! Clarissa Stone here, your lead Times Daily Tribune Broadcast Blog and Live Journal

Television and Interweb Reporter. I'm here with pre-teen rocket scientist — read: Anti-social — *(Beat.)* Herby Alice!

(She holds the microphone out to Herby. Consumed by his work, he does not respond in any way.)

(Hisses:) Herby! *(Beat.)* HERBY! *(Beat.)* Well, folks, what do you expect from a prodigy? *(Beat.)* No really. We want to know! Word on the street: wonderboy's discoveries may put our town on the map! Do you think he will accomplish what he claims? Or will we all witness his humiliating, fiery, and spectacular failure? Be sure to text us your vote, and post *your* comments at

www.TimesDailyTribuneBroadcastBlogandLiveJournal.com. *(Beat.)* Stay tuned, folks! And remember, you heard it here first. *(Beat.)* Count down to date of launch. TEN!

(Note: Each time a countdown number is given, it should be followed by an identifying sound — perhaps that of a rocket launching, or even a scale on the xylophone. This sound should stay the same for each number until noted at the end.)

(Camera Guy stops rolling.)

That's a wrap. *(Beat.)* Uggh! Herby, you are hopeless! This was supposed to be an interview! *(Beat.)* I'll just have to cobble something together. For now.

(Clarissa exits, Camera Guy on her heels. Rose finishes her notes, preparing to exit after Clarissa.)

HERBY: Sorry, did somebody say something?

ROSE: Who me? No! I — uh...have to go —

HERBY: Rose! I've been wanting to talk to you! I believe I'll be ready by the projected date, but I'm stuck on one of the final formulas. I could really use your mathematical acumen. Can you come by after school?

ROSE: I can't, Herby. I'm not—I uh, promised Clarissa I'd help edit blogs after school-

HERBY: What about tomorrow?

ROSE: I'm not really working on that sort of thing very much lately, Herby.

HERBY: *(Beat.)* Oh. Too bad. *(Beat.)* If you change your mind-

ROSE: Yeah. Sure. See you around.

(Rose exits. Herby resumes his work. STUDENTS 1 & 2 enter, speaking to the audience.)

STUDENT 1: *(Giggles:)* Dear Clarissa and Times Daily, all I have to say is: who wears a tie to school?

STUDENT 2: Dear Times. This whole thing is totally epic. I mean, talk about entertainment! What a freak. There's no way this is going to work. I mean, come on! Who does he think he is, NASA? *(Beat).* I vote no. He can't do it.

(Students 1 and 2 exit. Herby carefully places the object upon which he has been working on the stage. It is the base of the machine he is building. He exits.)

SCENE 2

(Clarissa enters, followed by Rose and Camera Guy. Camera Guy points the camera at Clarissa.)

CLARISSA: NINE!

(Sound effect. Students set up desks to create a classroom. The mirror should remain on stage, becoming the blackboard. Herby Alice sits at the front of the classroom and we see there is a sign on his back, which reads "Kick me." Other students are throwing wads of paper at Herby and laughing. He is hard at work building a second component of the machine. Rose sits at a desk behind him. MRS. PRATTLE, the teacher, dressed in

something ridiculous, enters. Clarissa takes her seat, motioning for the Camera Guy to train his camera on Herby.)

(In microphone:) Shhh! Let's observe our specimen in his natural habitat.

MRS. PRATTLE: Ding-dong! Can anyone tell me the capital of Bolivia? *(Beat.)* Or perhaps the market value of hedgehogs? *(Beat.)* Why are we here again?

(Mrs. Prattle consults her pocket watch.)

Gobbledy-gobbledy-gook. In 1978. And you weren't even born yet! But I had a Camaro. Or was it a canary? Either way it was yellow. Blah, blah, blah.

(Rose tries to get Herby's attention. Clarissa sees her.)

CLARISSA: *(To Rose:)* What are you doing?

ROSE: He's been wearing that neon orange sign all day...I have to say something.

CLARISSA: Have you never watched Animal Planet? Reporters do not interfere. NOT EVEN when the gazelle is being eaten by lions.

MRS. PRATTLE: Let me illustrate the principle for you on the chalkboard.

(Mrs. Prattle writes on the "chalkboard." She turns back to the class.)

(Triumphant:) Do you see?

(Dr. Faraway, the principal, also wearing something ridiculous, enters. He stands in the mirror frame, wearing a large grin. Turning back to the chalkboard, Mrs. Prattle is shocked to see him.)

Dr. Faraway! I didn't mean that kind of principal.

DR. FARAWAY: I am what I am and I say what I say! Has anyone here ever traveled through space?

(Everyone giggles. Mrs. Prattle distributes withering looks.)

MRS. PRATTLE: As I was saying...

(Dr. Faraway exits.)

Herby Alice, why don't *you* show them what I mean.

(Herby Alice walks to the front of the classroom, stepping through the mirror. He attaches a second piece of the component to the growing machine. The class giggles and whispers behind his back. Herby then turns in the mirror frame to face the class. The students quiet. Something in his manner stills them.)

CLARISSA: *(Hisses to Camera Guy:)* Get this on tape!

HERBY: The theory of relativity tells us that the faster you travel through space, the slower you travel through time. If one of us were to run around this classroom-

(Mrs. Prattle runs around classroom illustrating his point. Herby picks up after Mrs. Prattle is sitting.)

And if we were able to do so faster than the speed of light, first, you wouldn't even see the runner, but second, this individual would be an entire classroom revolution younger than they were before.

MRS. PRATTLE: Lovely! Any questions?

(All hands raise.)

Good! Class dismissed.

(Bell rings. Mrs. Prattle exits running. Kids begin to exit the classroom, confused. Herby is last. Rose waits.)

ROSE: Herby!

HERBY: Yes?

ROSE: You have a —

HERBY: Yeah, I know. I put it there. *(Beat.)* Quietest day I've had in weeks! But thanks.

(Camera Guy tapes Clarissa.)

CLARISSA: EIGHT!

(Sound effect. Camera Guy stops rolling. Clarissa notices Rose.)

Rose!

ROSE: *(To Herby:)* Gotta go —

HERBY: Bye, Rose.

(He exits.)

CLARISSA: What was THAT?

ROSE: Oh — nothing. I just had a question about...an assignment. That's all.

CLARISSA: You two used to be friends, didn't you?

ROSE: No! Well, when we were little kids.

CLARISSA: Weren't you friends, like, last year?

ROSE: Um...uh…

CLARISSA: This is perfect. JUST the angle I need.

ROSE: What? What do you mean?

CLARISSA: He respects you. Likes you, even. I can tell these things. I'm a scholar of human behavior.

ROSE: I don't understand.

CLARISSA: YOU can get me the interview I need.

ROSE: I don't think so, Clarissa —

CLARISSA: Alright. Fine. *(This is painful:)* I'll let you give the interview.

ROSE: You mean — you'll let me try again? On camera?

CLARISSA: But not live. And if you mess up, I'll edit you out. *(Beat.)* This is your chance.

ROSE: *(Takes a deep breath:)* Ok.

CLARISSA: You'll do it?

ROSE: Yes.

CLARISSA: Let's shake on it.

(They shake hands.)

But Rose, one thing?

ROSE: Yes?

CLARISSA: *(To Camera Guy:)* Get this on camera, please. I want a witness.

(Camera Guy rolls.)

I'm not going to have the Times Daily look like a bunch of yahoos.

ROSE: Um...okay?

CLARISSA: The media makes the story, Rose. Just like the historian writes the history. *(Beat.)* And let me be frank with you: the viewers make the ratings.

ROSE: Ratings? I thought only students and teachers watched our program.

CLARISSA: Today the school, tomorrow the world. *(Beat.)* Besides, we have to please The higher-ups. I promised. And I don't break my promises. *(Beat.)* Do you?

ROSE: No!

CLARISSA: Good. Now about the interview. Have you been reading the blogs?

ROSE: Of course! I've been editing them.

CLARISSA: Right. And you've been counting the votes?

ROSE: Yes.

CLARISSA: So you know that our viewers have certain expectations.

ROSE: They expect Herby to fail. Boy, are they going to be surprised when —

CLARISSA: Rose. Disappointing our viewers equals bad. Happy viewers equals good. Laughing at others makes the viewers feel better about themselves, and gives them a united purpose...thus bringing the community together and equaling happy viewers. Happy viewers equal happy executives. Happy executives mean happy Clarissa. Which means Rose gets to be somebody. And isn't that what you want? What you've been working toward?

ROSE: Yes...

CLARISSA: Then what am I asking from you?

ROSE: *(Beat.)* You want me to make Herby look like an idiot.

CLARISSA: Those are not my words, sweetie. The Times Daily would never say such a thing. It is our goal to deliver the news in the most impartial manner possible. *(To Camera Guy:)* Cut! *(She hands Rose the microphone.)* Go get me that interview. And it better be splashy.

ROSE: But — what if he doesn't fail? What if he succeeds?

CLARISSA: *(Beat.)* Well, we just need to make sure that doesn't happen, don't we? I'll leave that to you.

(Clarissa exits. Rose walks to mirror. She considers her outfit, her image. Unbeknownst to her, Camera Guy is still present. He starts rolling.)

ROSE: So tired of being invisible…(*To self:*) This could be your only chance, Rose. (*Notices Camera Guy:*) Hey! Stop the tape! Please – you have to edit that out.

(*Camera Guy runs off. Rose runs after him. UNPOPULAR STUDENT and POPULAR STUDENT enter.*)

UNPOPULAR STUDENT: Dear Clarissa, you are…prettier than a proton viewed through the magnetic lens of a transmission electron microscope…(*Beat.*) What? Oh! Yes. Sorry. My vote. I for one, have faith in Herby. I vote yes.

POPULAR STUDENT: Would you still vote yes from inside a garbage can?

(*Unpopular Student exits running. Popular Student chases after him.*)

SCENE 3

(*A gym whistle blows loudly. Dr. Faraway enters, blowing the whistle. Students follow at a jog. Popular Student has Unpopular Student in a headlock. Clarissa gestures for Rose to keep her sights on Herby. Herby, blind to the world, is working on another component of his machine. Rose holds the microphone. Camera Guy follows Rose. Mrs. Prattle enters running.*)

MRS. PRATTLE: Getting younger and younger! I LOVE gym class!

(*Mrs. Prattle exits running. The students line up and stretch. They are preparing for gym class to begin.*)

CLARISSA: (*Whispers:*) Rose! Go for it.

(*Clarissa moves off to stretch.*)

ROSE: Herby!

HERBY: (*Without looking up from his work:*) Yes, Rose?

ROSE: *(Holds out the microphone:)* Um...do you think I could grab a few words —

HERBY: I don't do interviews, Rose.

ROSE: But —

HERBY: However, if you've changed your mind about math, I could still use your help.

ROSE: Look — how about this: I'll help you with your project — if you give me this interview.

HERBY: No, thank you.

POPULAR STUDENT: Hey Rose!

ROSE: *(Wonderingly:)* He knows my name!

HERBY: How many years have we all gone to school together?

POPULAR STUDENT: When you're done talking with Alien Boy there — why don't you come over here and interview me! I've got mad skills!

HERBY: *(To Rose:)* Alien Boy? Clearly those "skills" include creative, poetic expression.

ROSE: *(Dreamily contemplating Popular Student:)* Yeah...

HERBY: *(Beat.)* Well, don't let me keep you from your fans.

ROSE: Okay...see you...

(Rose approaches Popular Student.)

CLARISSA: *(Whispers:)* Rose!

DR. FARAWAY: *(Blowing whistle.)* Today, marshmallows, we run! From the truth! At the speed of light!

(Mrs. Prattle runs by again.)

MRS. PRATTLE: Wheeeeeeeee!

(Mrs. Prattle exits running.)

DR. FARAWAY: SEVEN!

(Sound effect.)

I am what I am, and I say what I say — no one in my class will escape our fun play! Now, Rose, tell us all, did you get the interview?

(All the students turn to look at Rose, who is busy admiring Popular Student.)

ROSE: Huh?

DR. FARAWAY: Brilliant! You are a bright one. Can't wait to see your name in lights.

POPULAR STUDENT: *(To Rose:)* Can we do the interview in profile? I look amazing in profile.

DR. FARAWAY: Time to run! Let's cha-cha! Hurry it up, pickles!

(Dr. Faraway exits, blowing the whistle. All students besides Herby take off running. Herby sits at a desk to work. Rose follows Popular Student. Clarissa breaks in.)

CLARISSA: Rose! Dump this bozo! Go get me that interview!

(Clarissa gestures for Rose and Camera Guy to keep after Herby. Clarissa exits. Herby walks to his machine, attaching the component he has just finished. Herby exits.)

SCENE 4

(Rose sneaks over to Herby's machine to examine it.)

ROSE: Let's get a few shots of this. *(Beat.)* Zoom in on the combustion chamber.

(Camera Guy is at a loss. Rose points.)

This is where the chemical reaction takes place. I mean, I think that's, uh, where stuff happens? But wait a minute...this is a change from the plans I saw. In...class. Not like — at his house or anything. I mean we used to be friends when we were really little. But we don't run in the same, uh, crowd anymore. Since last — uh, kindergarten...and Herby didn't even start building interstellar rockets until first grade. *(Beat.)* Can you edit that out? *(Beat.)* Anyway...this doesn't look like it's just built to go to the moon, as he claims. This is built for something else. I don't even recognize this component. I wonder what this does —

(She accidently bends or breaks off a piece. She tries to fix it. She can't.)

Uh-oh. Turn off the camera. We have to get out of here.

(They start to sneak out. Herby enters, carrying another component.)

HERBY! I was...we were...just looking for you!

HERBY: Hello, Rose. Camera Guy.

ROSE: Um...just wanted to see if, you would, maybe reconsider the interview?

(Herby begins to attach the new piece to the machine. Camera Guy starts taping.)

HERBY: Wait a minute...that's not right...

ROSE: *(Quickly:)* Looks fine to me! Looks great!

(Rose steps in front of the machine.)

I heard that a professional scientist might show up at your launch?

HERBY: That's the rumor. We'll see.

(Herby tries to get around her.)

ROSE: That's really Cool, Herby. How do you feel about that?

(Rose points the microphone at Herby.)

HERBY: *(To Camera Guy:)* No cameras. *(Beat.)* I have work to do, Rose.

ROSE: *(To Camera Guy:)* You heard him!

(Camera Guy looks confused.)

No cameras! You'd better go see if you can help Clarissa.

(While Herby is working on the machine, Rose gestures for the Camera Guy to hide and keep rolling. He does so.)

HERBY: I know you aren't—participating—in "this sort of thing" right now, but if you could just hold up this screen while I screw in the bolt...*(Beat.)* Rose?

ROSE: Nothing—I...

HERBY: I'm about to drop this—you think you could—

ROSE: Okay. Yeah.

(She goes to help him.)

HERBY: Thank you, Rose. Thanks so much.

(She nods. Awkward silence.)

ROSE: So...is this part of your—

HERBY: Yes. This is the steering unit.

ROSE: Steering is good.

(Awkward silence.)

HERBY: *(Beat.)* Thanks. For helping.

ROSE: *(Beat.)* You...really think this...thing will...work?

HERBY: Well, if I can get that last pesky calculation worked out—the one I asked you about—

ROSE: Yeah...

HERBY: *(Beat.)* And if each and every piece is configured exactly to my original plan specifications, with no wire out of place. *(Beat.)* One off-kilter placement and — kablooey! My rocket and I will be sky kibble. Raining down like little squishy falling stars.

ROSE: Yuck.

HERBY: *(Beat.)* But I'm sure it will all work out just fine. *(Long beat.)* Something wrong?

ROSE: *(Squeaks:)* No! Just fine! *(Beat.)* But, do you...think it's a good idea to keep this here at school?

HERBY: Well, yes! It's the launch site!

ROSE: But what if...something happened to it?

HERBY: Oh, no one will touch it. They're all too afraid it will blow up or something.

(He laughs maniacally. She joins in, awkwardly.)

What do you think of it?

ROSE: Uh...it looks like you've made a lot of progress.

HERBY: Civilian space travel technology is advancing at the speed of light, Rose. I don't want to be left behind. Imagine — colonies on Mars, exploring extra solar planetary bodies, other celestial locales!

ROSE: *(Beat.)* This doesn't just look like your typical interstellar rocket, Herby. What are you really making here?

HERBY: I knew you'd pick up on that. *(Beat.)* But you wouldn't believe it if I told you.

ROSE: Try me.

(Herby Alice steps into the mirror frame. Enter ALIENS. Alien 1 approaches him, holding up the microphone. Enter eager cluster of additional aliens. One Alien holds a neon orange sign which reads "Welcome, Herby." He/she posts it on the front of Herby's shirt with a sense of ceremony.)

ALIENS: Bee bop boo bop beep. Beep. Beep. Boop.

ALIEN 1: In other words: Welcome, Herby!

ALIEN 2: We thought you'd never arrive!

ALIEN 1: Please, Herby, share your plans with your fans! The universe wants to know.

HERBY: First, we need independent interplanetary explorers. That's where I come in. If things go my way, the Magnum Stellar Z-T3 Hubber-Valley Alice Spacecraft Kit will be available online within 3-5 years. But first I have to get this baby off the ground.

ALIEN 1: But how will you...I mean...and isn't it, like, dangerous?

HERBY: Sure! But I know what I'm doing.

ALIEN 2: And your parents are okay with this.

HERBY: They're just sad there's not room for three passengers!

ALIEN 1: What about school?

HERBY: Well, if I travel as fast as I think I will, I'll be back before I left.

(Beat. Sound of explosion, either from offstage or recorded.)

ROSE: I think my brain just exploded. Did...you just say that you'll be back before you left?

HERBY: That's the plan!

ALIEN 1: Celestians, you heard it here first. Herby plans to be back before he leaves. *(Beat.)* Any questions?

(Explosion sounds again. Herby steps back through the mirror, sitting to resume work on his spacecraft.)

ROSE: So...this isn't just a rocket. It's...*(Reverentially:)* A time machine.

ALIENS: SIX!

(SOUND EFFECT.)

HERBY: The problem with colonizing other planets is NOT just an issue of atmosphere, or livable environs...we're finding plenty of planets we think might be quite comparable to our own. But—

ROSE: They are too far away.

HERBY: RIGHT! My machine would travel faster than the speed of light, utilizing wormholes for further shortcuts.

ROSE: But this has far-reaching implications! I mean—this could totally change the world as we know it! I mean—time machines? Worm holes? Space-time continuum! If things went wrong—couldn't time collapse in on itself, thus rendering us non-existent and destroying us all?

HERBY: Which is why this information can't fall into the wrong hands.

ROSE: That's why you won't do interviews.

HERBY: You got it.

(Camera Guy turns off his camera. He's got what he needs. He sneaks out. Rose sees him, but Herby doesn't.)

ROSE: But—don't you think people deserve to know about such life-altering scientific discoveries?

HERBY: Rose, I'm not even sure yet if it will work.

ROSE: Well, if it does, it changes everything.

ALIENS: Herby, Herby, he's our man! He'll change the Universe, fast as he can! Be bop! Boop beep bop boop beep!

ROSE: *(Beat.)* Herby. You should hear the things kids say about you. I mean actually — you shouldn't, I guess.

HERBY: What do I care?

ROSE: Well — I mean, with an interview, you could set things straight —

HERBY: Does it really matter what they think? In the greater scheme of things?

ROSE: *(Beat.)* Yes. No. I don't know…they can sure make life hard in the meantime.

(Herby sits on his desk, looking thoughtfully up at the sky.)

HERBY: Some nights when I can't sleep I carry my telescope outside to my tree house.

(The Aliens sit, mimicking Herby's position, also looking thoughtfully up at the sky.)

I spend hours…just looking into space. And you know something? As long as I stay, I never see any more than the smallest portion of what's out there.

(Rose looks thoughtfully up at the sky.)

ROSE: *(Beat.)* Herby, I —

HERBY: I'm sorry I pressured you about helping me. We're on different paths now. I understand that. I guess…I just — miss the way it was, you know, when we were kids? Last year? You've always been my best friend. But now…well, I guess you're pretty busy with the media circus. You've got your new friends. Your extracurricular activities. Your new — look.

ROSE: *(She adjusts her outfit self-consciously:)* It was Clarissa's idea. She thought it'd be more—camera friendly. *(Long beat, defensively:)* I was tired of feeling invisible all the time!

HERBY: You have never been invisible to me. *(Beat.)* You'll be great at broadcasting. Just like you are at everything. And I won't tell anybody that you still get straight As in math and science.

(They laugh.)

ROSE: Thanks. *(Beat.)* Um, Herby? I, uh...that piece on your machine?

(She points to it.)

HERBY: Yeah, I noticed.

ROSE: I'm really sorry. I should have told you.

HERBY: *(Smiling:)* It's fine. I can fix it.

ROSE: *(Beat.)* Herby—I—

HERBY: Yes?

ROSE: I uh—I...I'll let you get back to work.

HERBY: *(Beat.)* See you.

(Dr. Faraway and Mrs. Prattle enter running as Rose exits.)

DR. FARAWAY: Run from the truth as fast as you can! At the speed of light, you can't be outran! *(Calling encouragingly after Herby:)* Through the wormhole!

MRS. PRATTLE & DR. FARAWAY: FIVE!

(SOUND EFFECT.)

MRS. PRATTLE: We're halfway there!

(Mrs. Prattle exits running.)

SCENE 5

(Clarissa enters holding a video. Mrs. Prattle re-enters running. She stops, out of breath.)

CLARISSA: Rose! I got the video of your interview! I can't wait to watch it. From what I understand, it's brilliant! Maybe you aren't a total waste of time after all!

ROSE: Um...thanks.

CLARISSA: And Alien Boy didn't even know you were interviewing him!

ROSE: No. He didn't.

CLARISSA: Hidden camera!? Didn't know you had it in you. Maybe... I'll even let you cover the launch on Friday.

ROSE: Me? Live?

DR. FARAWAY: Big news! The whole school will be watching!

MRS. PRATTLE: Even one second can be eternity in front of a crowd! Hopefully you won't fall flat on your face.

ROSE: In front of a crowd...?

MRS. PRATTLE: —Faint dead away—

DR. FARAWAY: —like the student at the beginning of the year.

MRS. PRATTLE: Oh yes. There she stood...blabbering on about the crisis in Oblivia, or was it Alabama? Remember how terribly she froze? The students in the control room laughing and laughing—

(Beat while RECORDED OR OFFSTAGE LAUGHTER bubbles up. It ends abruptly when Rose speaks.)

ROSE: That was me, Mrs. Prattle.

MRS. PRATTLE: Oooooh! Dear. How embarrassing for us all.

CLARISSA: I had to fight the establishment tooth and nail after that to keep student control of the Times Daily.

MRS. PRATTLE: Bravo!! You really stuck it to us!

DR. FARAWAY: Well, I'm certain this time you will comport yourself with dignity and deviled eggs.

CLARISSA: You'd better.

DR. FARAWAY: I am what I am, and I say what I say—

MRS. PRATTLE: Rose Plum is a peach of a pumpkin tea tray!

CLARISSA: This could lead to a beautiful partnership, Rose.

    (Clarissa exits.)

ROSE: Wait! Clarissa! Can I watch the video before you air it? I'm not so sure—

MRS. PRATTLE: *(Advancing menacingly:)* No pressure—

DR. FARAWAY: But the fate of the world rests in your hands.

MRS. PRATTLE: IF your interview fails to deliver, you will be de-pantsed in the cafeteria at high noon.

DR. FARAWAY: *(Terribly worried:)* What if she doesn't wear pants? What if she wears a dress? Or a skirt?

MRS. PRATTLE: *(Shocked:)* For all we know she won't even be carrying an umbrella!

    (Dr. Faraway blows twice on his gym whistle.)

DR. FARAWAY: Come now, Dearie-Do! Weren't we running from the truth?

MRS. PRATTLE: How delightful!

DR. FARAWAY: No ifs, ands, or elbows about it. Let's fly!

    (Dr. Faraway and Mrs. Prattle exit running.)

SCENE 6

(Rose sits at her desk, preparing for her next class, and for the tape to air. Aliens enter, circling Rose in a menacing fashion.)

ALIENS: *(Threateningly:)* Be bop boop bop beep booooop bip bip BIP!

ALIEN 1: Everyone deserves to know the truth.

ALIEN 2: What choice did you have?

ALIEN 1: Sure the information might fall into the wrong hands...

ALIEN 2: But don't worry. Who is even going to believe it?

ALIEN 1: He's going to be a laughing stock.

ALIEN 2: What's a laughing stalk? Is it anything like a beanstalk?

ROSE: Uh...

ALIEN 2: You'll be the one who brought him down.

ALIEN 1: And he still thinks of you as his best friend!

ALIENS: HILARIOUS! *(Alien laughter:)* Beep beep beep!

ALIEN 2: What's one measly human, in the scheme of things?

ALIEN 1: Especially when you are SO close to the life you want!

ALIEN 2: If you want to be somebody, you've got to be willing to draw blood.

ALIEN 1: Gross!

ALIEN 2: I meant that metaphorically.

ALIEN 1: Oh! Thank goodness.

ALIEN 2: I mean unless this rocket thing doesn't work right, and Herby *does* end up exploding into a million tiny pieces.

ALIEN 1: OPTION C: say someone DOES believe him...and say it's the worst kind of person...and say they get a hold of his time travel discoveries and use them for evil gain...she could be responsible for the destruction of the entire universe and everything in it.

ALIEN 2: Well, you win some, you lose some.

ALIENS: Rose the Destroyer!

(Alien laughter, either live or boosted by sound effects.)

(Herby enters, carrying another component of the machine. He attaches it.)

HERBY: Hi, Rose!

(Dr. Faraway enters running. He and Mrs. Prattle are racing. Mrs. Prattle pulls ahead.)

MRS. PRATTLE: FOUR!

(Sound effect. Mrs. Prattle exits, leaving Dr. Faraway in the dust.)

DR. FARAWAY: That canary flies faster than moon rocks! By now she must be 20 years younger than me! If I could turn back time...

(Dr. Faraway exits. Popular Student enters, with Unpopular Student still in a headlock. He sits at his desk [with Unpopular Student still in a headlock].)

POPULAR STUDENT: You know, everybody is going to be listening on Friday.

ALIENS 1 & 2: The whole universe.

UNPOPULAR STUDENT: This is your chance, Rose! Do it for the little guy! Show us we can escape our lowly circumstances. *(To Popular Student:)* Ouch! Could you let up a little? You're twisting my retainer...

(Enter Dr. Faraway, very out of breath, but still running.)

DR. FARAWAY: Oh, the sport! I am what I am. Say what I say, we'd better get moving without a delay! Let's move, lobsters! Remember, Rose — through the wormhole!

(He exits, still running. Clarissa enters and sits at her desk. Herby stands in the mirror frame, addressing the class.)

CLARISSA: Just picture it.

HERBY: *(Envisioning:)* The wormhole. The absolute dark unknown. A tunnel of space-time that maybe, just maybe, will connect you to the farthest stretch of the universe, possibly even whole other universes. Then. Deciding. To take the plunge. It's so...astrophysical.

POPULAR STUDENT: *(Laughing uproariously:)* OMG! He's better than reality TV! And the comedy channel! Rolled into one! *(To Unpopular Student:)* Go get me some popcorn.

(Unpopular Student exits running. On Herby's next line, the loud SOUND OF A CLOCK TICKING should begin. It speeds up, getting faster and faster.)

HERBY: *(To Audience:)* Fact: a perfectly functional atomic clock traveling at an extreme velocity has been measured to move more slowly than a perfectly functional atomic clock at rest.

(The Aliens advance upon Rose.)

ALIENS: BEE BOP BEEP! What's it gonna be, Rose? BEE BOP BEEP!

ALIEN 1: You could still stop the tape from airing—

ALIEN 2: *(Sing-song:)* No decision is still a decision, Rose...

(Unpopular Student enters with popcorn. He whispers in Clarissa's ear. Popular Student puts him back in a headlock and begins eating the popcorn.)

CLARISSA: Oh, guess what! Too late! Just in: the button has been pushed. And that button, was play...So let's sit back, and enjoy the ride! Arms and legs inside the vehicle. Buckle your seatbelts, friends. You're about to see the interview of your life!

ROSE: But wait—what if the wrong person gets a hold of this information? What if the machine blows up? What if—

HERBY: What if we could determine the time...instead of the time determining us?

CLARISSA: Just concentrate on your job, Rose. If you play things right...You will be...

ALIENS: A star!

HERBY: What is time when you are among the stars?

POPULAR STUDENT: Rose, you are the greatest. Rose! Rose! Rose!

ALIEN 1: A Rose by any other name—

ALIEN 2: Would still smell like betrayal.

(Enter Mrs. Prattle.)

MRS. PRATTLE: THREE!

(SOUND EFFECT.)

(Dr. Faraway enters running, still out of breath.)

DR. FARAWAY: Run! Run! Let's watch Herby and Rose on the talky-box!

MRS. PRATTLE: Have you heard? Herby Alice is building a canary! Or is it a tree house?

(Everyone exits running except Herby, Rose, and the Aliens. The now frantic TICKING of the clock ends. Herby puts the last

component on the machine, then, stands in the mirror frame. All of the Aliens gather around him.)

(We hear an offstage recording of Herby and Rose's interview. If they have the resources, the producing company could also broadcast this excerpt from "the interview.")

ROSE (O.S.): If used incorrectly, couldn't time collapse in on itself, thus rendering us non-existent...destroying us all?

HERBY (O.S.): Which is why this information can't fall into the wrong hands.

(The Aliens exit, disgusted with Rose.)

ROSE: Herby — *(Beat.)* Herby! *(Beat.)* Listen, I —

HERBY: Enough. Please go away.

ROSE: I'm sorry... I didn't know the sensitive nature of the project —

(Enter Aliens 1 and 2.)

ALIEN 1: Did you hear? Clarissa posted the broadcast on YouTube, and a real live astrophysicist saw Herby, and is coming to our school! To Herby's launch! If the machine works — they are going to confiscate it! Visit other planets! Meet aliens! Travel through time!

ALIEN 2: Everyone knows there is no such thing as aliens.

ALIEN 1: *(Defensively:)* Well, that's just what I heard.

(Aliens exit.)

ROSE: Herby! I've got it! Why don't you just cancel the launch?

HERBY: *(Sarcastic:)* Brilliant. Why didn't I think of that? *(Beat.)* First of all, conditions for the test run were a precise calculation. If I don't do this on Friday, I can't test it for another 11 years, 33 days, 56 minutes, and 27 seconds.

Additionally, and the old you would have figured this out by now, the only damage control at this point is a fully operational time machine.

ROSE: *(Beat.)* Did...did you work out that last calculation?

HERBY: I think so.

ROSE: But you're not sure?

HERBY: That's just the risk I'll have to take.

ROSE: And if it isn't right?

HERBY: Kablooey.

ROSE: I'll help you—you thought I might be able to help—maybe I still can—

HERBY: Like how an iceberg "helped" the titanic? Thanks anyway.

ROSE: You wouldn't help me either, you know! You could have given me that interview. You wouldn't have had to spill everything. In fact—this never would have happened if—

HERBY: You know what? The simple truth is—and I don't know why I didn't see this before—you have just changed more than I realized. Into someone I don't know, and don't particularly like.

ROSE: You—you think you're so smart—but you know what? If you really were, you would have trusted me—

HERBY: *(Snorts:)* Trusted you?

ROSE: I could have helped—I could have gotten the other kids to take you seriously—

HERBY: You just don't get it.

ROSE: You know what? I bet it doesn't work! It's a ridiculous idea anyway. No way it works. You'll just be stuck here in cold reality, on planet earth, like everybody else! You are going to be completely humiliated! And I can't wait to watch!

(Herby angrily throws a blanket over his machine.)

(Beat.) Herby, wait — I didn't mean it —

(The students re-enter, led by Popular Student and Clarissa.)

POPULAR STUDENT: Rose! That was brilliant! I love the way you got him to talk by pretending to know the geek-lingo! For a second there you really had me going. You are hilarious!

UNPOPULAR STUDENT: Rose, can I be your assistant? Here, let me carry your clipboard!

CLARISSA: Ahem! For the record — I made her everything she is today, you know. She learned it all from me!

(The students pick Rose up, cheering for her.)

CROWD: Rose! Rose! Rose!

(They carry her offstage. Clarissa finds herself alone with Herby.)

CLARISSA: For what it's worth — *(Beat.)* I voted yes.

(Herby exits, disgusted. Finding herself alone, Clarissa exits in the opposite direction. The students return, strike the desks, then, and exit. Mrs. Prattle wanders in.)

MRS. PRATTLE: TWO!

(SOUND EFFECT.)

Class dismissed! *(Beat.)* Where is everybody going? People come and go so quickly here.

(She wanders offstage.)

SCENE 7

(Rose enters, carrying tools and a box. She lifts the blanket on the machine, and changes something.)

ROSE: That...should do it!

(Clarissa enters.)

CLARISSA: Oooh! You are much more dangerous than I realized. Guess I'll have to watch my back!

(Rose quickly re-covers the machine. She sets the box by her feet. Camera Guy and other students enter, giggling, whispering, and laughing to themselves. Mrs. Prattle and Dr. Faraway enter. Finally, the Camera Guy trains the camera on Rose. He hands Rose the microphone.)

MRS. PRATTLE: Nervous, ducky?

ROSE: *(Takes a deep breath:)* Nope, I'm ready to go.

MRS. PRATTLE: I brought smelling salts in case she faints! Jubilation!

DR. FARAWAY: Should have run when you could, marshmallow!

CLARISSA: Ready Rose?

ROSE: Yes.

CLARISSA: Then let's roll! Action!

ROSE: Welcome, everyone! To the test launch of the Magnum Stellar Z-T3 Hubber-Valley Alice Spacecraft.

(The students laugh. DR. TOMORROW, an astrophysicist enters carrying a clipboard.)

Welcome, to all of you. Especially to our visiting guest, Dr. Tomorrow.

(Rose hands Dr. Tomorrow the microphone.)

DR. TOMORROW: If this young man accomplishes what he claims he can, well, we're all going to be a lot richer!

(Everyone laughs.)

Especially me!

(Everyone claps politely. Mrs. Prattle and Dr. Faraway take turns posing with Dr. Tomorrow and taking pictures.)

ROSE: Where's Herby?

CLARISSA: There he is!

(Herby enters. The Aliens follow. They pull the blanket off the finished machine.)

CROWD: Oooh! Ahhh!

(Herby approaches Rose.)

ROSE: Herby —

(Herby takes her microphone.)

Wait, what —

(Clarissa gestures to Camera Guy to train his camera on Herby.)

HERBY: Welcome everyone.

(Mrs. Prattle dances with joy.)

MRS. PRATTLE: Glee! I love a recital. I once had to recite a poem backwards. I finished before I even began.

HERBY: You aren't going to remember this, so what I'm about to say won't make any difference. But I'm going to share nonetheless. *(To Rose:)* You wanted an interview? Here goes. You think what everybody else thinks is so important. But guess what? News flash. The only opinion about you that matters? Is yours. Maybe someday you'll figure that out.

(Herby shoves the microphone back at Rose. He presses the start button on the machine. We hear the engine fire up.)

Start the countdown!

CROWD: TEN!

(There are no sound effects during this countdown until the end. More and more people drop out of the countdown each time, until the end when only the Aliens say: "lift off". Herby starts to put on his space helmet. Mrs. Prattle runs in a circle.)

MRS. PRATTLE: Oh joy! I can't wait to run into yesteryear! I'm not going to remember anything!

CROWD: NINE!

(Dr. Tomorrow approaches the spacecraft.)

HERBY: Sir, I'm going to have to ask you to step away from the launch-site.

DR. TOMORROW: I'm going with you.

CROWD: EIGHT!

HERBY: What? I don't even know you!

DR. TOMORROW: Why, I'm Dr. Tomorrow! Professional astrophysicist. I've authored books! Dined with diplomats! Invented new elements!

CROWD: SEVEN!

(Rose steps forward. She opens the box she brought, and takes out a space helmet.)

ROSE: *(To Dr. Tomorrow:)* I'm sorry, but you can't go with him! Because I am.

HERBY: What? No! Neither of you can come with me — the rocket is fit to my exact body specifications —

DR. TOMORROW: A clever boy like you could easily adjust the settings.

ROSE: It's already adjusted, Herby. I fixed it to include two passengers. You and me.

CROWD: SIX!

HERBY: You TAMPERED with the Magnum Stellar??

ALIENS: Kablooey!

ROSE: Your calculation was wrong, Herby! This thing would have blown you sky high! I fixed it. Now please—let me help you fix the mess I made—

HERBY: Why should I trust you?

CROWD: FIVE!

ROSE: *(Beat.)* Because—you're the best friend I've ever had!

DR. TOMORROW: There is no room for friendship in science, young man. Friends are a distraction, a liability. They'll only steal your ideas, and burn your time. Take my word. I am a professional scientist! Just think of where I could take your career! *(Beat. To Rose:)* Hand over the helmet, girlie.

(Dr. Tomorrow advances menacingly toward Rose, grabbing at the helmet.)

CROWD: FOUR!

HERBY: You leave her alone!

(Herby grabs Dr. Tomorrow's coat. The helmet drops to the ground. Herby picks it up and Dr. Tomorrow tries to wrestle it out of his hands.)

CLARISSA: *(To Camera Guy:)* Be sure to get this! This is a front-pager!

CROWD: THREE!

DR. TOMORROW: Give me the helmet!

(Rose snatches the helmet out of Dr. Tomorrow's hands, and grabs Herby.)

ROSE: Come on, Herby!

(Hand in hand, they race toward the spacecraft.)

CROWD: TWO!

(They stand in the mirror frame. Dr. Tomorrow runs after them. The Aliens hold Dr. Tomorrow back.)

DR. TOMORROW: NO!!!

ALIENS: LIFT OFF!

(Loud SOUND EFFECT of ROCKET LAUNCH. This should last longer than the earlier sound effects for each countdown. During the sound effect the crowd should act as if they are watching an actual rocket launch in the audience, their gazes following it up into the sky. The Aliens take hands. Everyone exits, except Rose and Herby. They stand in the mirror a moment longer. They smile at each other. Then, finally, they step through the mirror together, and exit. The Aliens enter, walking backwards. They un-build the machine, exiting with the pieces. Dr. Faraway enters while they are un-building the machine. He is wearing his cat-smile. He stands in the mirror frame.)

DR. FARAWAY: We are what we are, and we say what we say, speeding faster than light into yester-today...

(Dr. Faraway exits, as Herby Alice, a student and rocket scientist, enters. He wears a necktie as usual. He is totally focused on fixing a component of a high-tech contraption he is building. He stands in the mirror frame. Clarissa, lead student reporter, enters. She is brushing her perfect hair and powdering her perfect nose. She is followed by Camera Guy, and Rose.)

CLARISSA: *(To Rose:)* How do I look?

ROSE: *(Laughing:)* I would bet the thermal properties of your blazer are exceptionally beneficial in algid weather!

CLARISSA: You are a fixer-upper, aren't you?

ROSE: *(Laughs:)* Yep!

(Rose and Herby take hands, and exit, laughing. Mrs. Prattle runs by.)

MRS. PRATTLE: Pretty soon, I'll be so young, they're going to have to teach me! Ho ho! Hee hee...

(Mrs. Prattle exits running. Lights out. End of play.)

The Author Speaks

What inspired you to write this play?
I wrote *Herby Alice Counts Down to Yesterday* in my MFA program, in a Youth Plays class taught by Jon Dorf. I wanted to write a play that would be performable by middle school students, and have always been fascinated by physics theories (especially time travel). As an enrichment teacher and librarian, I am also delighted by the unlimited imaginations and brilliance of young thinkers and emerging eccentrics. I wanted to tell the story of one brilliant oddball, and a friend of his who has to choose between following the crowd or being herself.

Was the structure of the play influenced by any other work?
Herby Alice Counts Down to Yesterday was influenced by my class with Jon Dorf, and by his work writing plays for young performers. Although I have helped young writers develop their own works, this was the first time I had written "alone" for the youth actor market. I was experimenting with creating a flexible cast in number of actors and gender, with each part and "potential part" being roles that would offer a fun challenge, or moment in the spotlight, for its actor. I also wanted to write a play with a "time bomb" structure. The countdown to the rocket's launch creates the underlying pace.

Have you dealt with the same theme in other works that you have written?
One constant theme in all my plays is a protagonist who is deciding what kind of person they are going to be. I find this particular kind of genesis—the moments in which we makes strides toward self-definition, to be the most fascinating aspect of growing up and learning about life and self. I also usually have a protagonist or a major character with a passion for some subject/career (a scientist, a storyteller, a musician, etc.),

and sometimes another character who is struggling to find/articulate their own niche/passion.

What writers have had the most profound effect on your style?

Hmm...that is a difficult question. I am a voracious reader, so I would say that my style is influenced by countless writers!! I can cite particular works that have profoundly helped shape my world view, as well as the underlying themes in my plays and stylistic choices. I think most notably, as a child I read every fairy tale, collection of myths, and fantasy/sci-fi novel I could get my hands on. I also loved historical fiction. Probably all of my plays reflect these genre fascinations to some degree. Works (plays and novels) that have "changed me" or affected my writing include: *Ender's Game* by Orson Scott Card, *The Light Princess* by George MacDonald, anything by Hans Christian Anderson, D'Aulaire's *Book of Greek Myths*, *East of Eden* by John Steinbeck, *The Yellow Boat* by David Saar, *The Commedia Princess and the Pea* by Lane Riosey and Rebecca Byers, *Little Medea* by Melissa Cooper, and Shakespeare, because of the summer I spent studying and deciphering his work in London, and because of the Shakespeare in the Park I did as a middle school student. When it comes to plays, my writing has been perhaps most affected by the staging of them—both in the writing, and by producing companies. I am totally enamored of "stage-magic." Not just Cirque de Soleil-style choreography (though I love beautiful movement), but simple things. I remember the delicious and horrifying thrill of hearing the dull, arresting thud of a cantaloupe that was thrown to the stage floor, as a head was "chopped off" in a Shakespeare play staging. For a second, I really thought there had been a beheading! Live! In a theatre! I saw that and thought—man, in plays you can do anything.

What do you hope to achieve with this work?
With all my plays, I hope first and foremost to enchant the audience and producers. I want them to laugh, feel, think, and to be spirited away a little. I want them to experience the work and then later think — "man, in plays you can do anything!" I would also like them to contemplate themselves, and perhaps even...change a little.

What are the most common mistakes that occur in productions of your work?
The producers approach everything literally, and don't look for ways to enhance the work with their own discoveries. A play is a blueprint — a picture in black and white that is waiting to have its colors filled in by the technicians, actors, and then emotionally finished/filled out by audience response. The producing company should look for imaginative ways to achieve the "stage magic" and to attain authenticity in interpreting the characters. HOWEVER: the other mistake that I see with my plays and with the production of new plays in general, is that a producing company does not fully do their homework. They should know the play through and through, work to puzzle/decipher/research what may have influenced the writer (maybe mythology, or history, or references to topical events, etc.). Every member of a producing company should always dive into the world of the play and try to articulate what the play is about. When they can do that, then every decision can be made confidently, because it arises out of the vision/strength of the play, and not from some superimposed vision that has nothing to do with the heart of the play or what it might be ultimately saying.

What inspired you to become a playwright?
I have acted in theatre since I was four years old, continuing since as a writer, actor, teacher, technician, director, etc...I have

seen time and time again how affecting theatre can be—for its participants, and for its audience. I have also been writing and reading prolifically since I was seven. These areas of interest have merged naturally over the years...I think I've always been a playwright. As to pursuing it professionally, I would really love one day to see original theatre for youth being as popular as books or movies...I mean, why not? It offers a completely different experience! I also think youth deserve plays that are as fresh, exciting, and dangerous—in other words, as cogent, as the plays offered to adult audiences. I think everybody deserves theatre at its best! That is my aim as a writer, to make exciting theatre, encourage other writers to do the same, and to be a part of a larger movement and discussion.

How did you research the subject?

As I mentioned, I'm a reader. I read all the time, and every time I write a play I read a lot in that subject area to get my mind in the right place. With *Herby Alice* I also looked at a lot of NASA websites and read about rocket launches.

Shakespeare gave advice to the players in *Hamlet*; if you could give advice to your cast what would it be?

Explore the range of emotions in each of the characters. I like to write about passionate people. I am also a big fan of finding the humor in things—especially "the 180." I think one of the funniest things in the world is to watch people instantly change their mind or demeanor. And I think humor can be found in the most unexpected places. That's why I enjoy Shakespeare so much—he was funny ALL THE TIME! And because we have a limited understanding of the language, we often miss the humor until we do our homework. I think that happens in everyday language, too! So, do your homework, and have the time of your life!

About the Author

Children's Program Coordinator and Children's Playwright in Residence at SkyPilot Theatre in Los Angeles, **Nicole B. Adkins** holds her MFA in Children's Literature with an emphasis in playwriting from Hollins University. She has a BA in Theatre Arts from the University of Central Oklahoma, and studied Shakespeare at London Academy of Music and Dramatic Arts. A playwright for youth and adults, Nicole has worked with children's theatres as a performer and teacher for over a decade. She is a winner of the 2011 National Waldo M. and Grace C. Bonderman Playwriting Workshop, was invited to participate in the 2009 Bonderman Symposium Playwright Slam, and has been showcased in the annual Best of No Shame Theatre Virginia. She is a member of The Dramatists Guild of America, Inc., Theatre for Young Audiences/USA, Alliance of Los Angeles Playwrights, and the Society of Children's Book Writers and Illustrators. Website: www.nicolebadkins.com.

About YouthPLAYS

YouthPLAYS (www.youthplays.com) is a publisher of award-winning professional dramatists and talented new discoveries, each with an original theatrical voice, and all dedicated to expanding the vocabulary of theatre for young actors and audiences. On our website you'll find one-act and full-length plays and musicals for teen and pre-teen (and even college) actors, as well as duets and monologues for competition. Many of our authors' works have been widely produced at high schools and middle schools, youth theatres and other TYA companies, both amateur and professional, as well as at elementary schools, camps, churches and other institutions serving young audiences and/or actors worldwide. Most are intended for performance by young people, while some are intended for adult actors performing for young audiences.

YouthPLAYS was co-founded by professional playwrights Jonathan Dorf and Ed Shockley. It began merely as an additional outlet to market their own works, which included a substantial body of award-winning published and unpublished plays and musicals. Those interested in their published plays were directed to the respective publishers' websites, and unpublished plays were made available in electronic form. But when they saw the desperate need for material for young actors and audiences—coupled with their experience that numerous quality plays for young people weren't finding a home—they made the decision to represent the work of other playwrights as well. Dozens and dozens of authors are now members of the YouthPLAYS family, with scripts available both electronically and in traditional acting editions. We continue to grow as we look for exciting and challenging plays and musicals for young actors and audiences.

About ProduceaPlay.com

Let's put up a play! Great idea! But producing a play takes time, energy and knowledge. While finding the necessary time and energy is up to you, ProduceaPlay.com is a website designed to assist you with that third element: knowledge.

Created by YouthPLAYS' co-founders, Jonathan Dorf and Ed Shockley, ProduceaPlay.com serves as a resource for producers at all levels as it addresses the many facets of production. As Dorf and Shockley speak from their years of experience (as playwrights, producers, directors and more), they are joined by a group of award-winning theatre professionals and experienced teachers from the world of academic theatre, all making their expertise available for free in the hope of helping this and future generations of producers, whether it's at the school or university level, or in community or professional theatres.

The site is organized into a series of major topics, each of which has its own page that delves into the subject in detail, offering suggestions and links for further information. For example, Publicity covers everything from Publicizing Auditions to How to Use Social Media to Posters to whether it's worth hiring a publicist. Casting details Where to Find the Actors, How to Evaluate a Resume, Callbacks and even Dealing with Problem Actors. You'll find guidance on your Production Timeline, The Theater Space, Picking a Play, Budget, Contracts, Rehearsing the Play, The Program, House Management, Backstage, and many other important subjects.

The site is constantly under construction, so visit often for the latest insights on play producing, and let it help make your play production dreams a reality.

More from YouthPLAYS

The Story Club by Nicole B. Adkins
Young Audiences. 45-50 minutes. 1 male, 3 females.

Ivy is used to being the Queen of the Story Club. Everyone agrees she's the best storyteller—that's why *she* gets to make up the stories and cast the parts. But the Queen's subjects are suddenly getting restless: little brother Charlie won't stop practicing karate, her friend Justine starts to get ideas of her own, and then a clever new neighbor arrives just in time to take over Fairy Land!

The Old New Kid by Adam J. Goldberg
Comedy. 30-40 minutes. 2-9+ males, 3-10+ females (8-30+ performers possible).

It's the half-day of school before Thanksgiving break, and current "new kid" Alan Socrates Bama just wants to get through the day. But when a new-new kid arrives, things change. Alan has three hours to find the meaning of Thanksgiving, survive elementary school politics, battle for his identity, and spell the word "cornucopia" in this *Peanuts*-flavored comedy for kids of all ages.

No Good Deed Goes Unpunished by Cheryl Hadley
Comedy. 40-50 minutes. 4-32 males, 8-32 females (12-48 performers possible).

Kind, level-headed Widgina always seems to be in the wrong place at the wrong time. Everywhere she goes, things go terribly wrong and people end up mistaking her for a witch! As she narrates her story and classic fairy tale characters come and go, can Widgina finally get the happily ever after she deserves?

The Unscary Ghost by Matt Buchanan
Comedy. 40-50 minutes. 3+ males, 5+ females, 8+ either (13-30+ performers possible).

Loosely based on Oscar Wilde's *The Canterville Ghost*. When the Otis family moves into the old Victorian home in Canterville, Ohio, they soon learn that the place is haunted—by a ghost who can't scare anyone. The jaded, modern family alternately taunts and tries to exploit the unfortunate ghost, Simon Canter, even trying to get a spot on the hit TV show, *America's Most Haunted*. Only the oldest daughter, Ginny, seems to care for or understand poor Simon. Can she help him find peace? A sometimes zany, sometimes touching show for the whole family.

Roll of Thunder, Hear My Cry by Ed Shockley
Drama. 105-115 minutes. 6+ males, 4+ females (12-40 performers possible).

The gripping story of Cassie Logan's coming of age in Jim Crow Mississippi is brought to life on the stage. A cast of ten principal actors plus an expandable chorus performing in a stark setting transform this epic into an inspiring tale of hope and triumph in the face of adversity.

The Jungle Book by Callan Stout
Adaptation. 70-75 minutes. 6-22 males, 2-8 females (7-24 performers possible).

In this adaptation of Kipling's famous stories, the beat of a drum and the cry of a wolf give way to the sounds of the ferocious tiger Shere Khan on the hunt. But when the wolf pack discovers that he is hunting a human child, they rescue the infant Mowgli from the tiger's teeth. Mother and Father Wolf adopt the man-cub, and with the protection of Bagheera the panther and the teachings of Baloo the bear, Mowgli lives peacefully with the wolves. But as he grows into manhood, he will not be able to escape his inevitable showdown with Shere Khan.

Miracle in Mudville by D.W. Gregory
Comedy. 60-70 minutes. 5-11+ males, 13-17+ females, 3+ either (21-31+ performers possible).

Casey is the worst ballplayer in the Mudville Little League, the butt of jokes and an embarrassment to his dad, who brags of his glory days in the outfield. But he's not alone in feeling inadequate; his friends Murphy and Hector suffer by comparison to their parents, too. Then a chance encounter with the ghost of the town's dead librarian throws Casey and his friends into a time warp—where they discover that some of their parents' big adventures didn't quite happen the way they said...

Dancing With Myself by Leanne Griffin
Dramedy. 35-45 minutes. 7 females.

Goth Girl. Moody Chick. Gamer. Cheerleader. New Kid. Jock. Nerd. Seven high school girls and the labels they've been forced to wear. But in this innovative, award-winning dramedy, whether it's sports or a sleepover or the classroom or a school dance or the ups and downs of daily life, they'll use music as their inspiration to break free of the stereotypes and discover the unique identity they each possess.

Calamity by E. J. C. Calvert
Comedy. 50-60 minutes. 3 females, 4-12+ either (7-15+ performers possible).

Twelve-year-old Calamity Jane and her mother are on their way to California when they find themselves in the beleaguered town of Hoopersville. With all but a trio of townsfolk kidnapped by the hilariously hair-raising hoopsnakes, can Calamity Jane rally the remaining townspeople out of their hidey-holes to face the Hoopsnake Queen and rescue the populace, or will they too end up as dinner-in-waiting?

72233040R00028

Made in the USA
Columbia, SC
15 June 2017